Kwork Kwork the Green Frog

Kwork

Kwork

the Green Frog
and other tales
from the Spirit Time

Australian National University Press, Canberra 1977

First published in Australia 1977

Printed in Singapore for the Australian
National University Press, Canberra

This book was published with the support of
the Aboriginal Arts Board

National Library of Australia
Cataloguing-in-Publication entry

Kwork Kwork the Green Frog and other
tales from the Spirit Time.
For Children.
ISBN 0 7081 0360 x.
[1.] Aborigines, Australian—Legends—
Juvenile literature.
398.20994

Southeast Asia: Angus & Robertson
(S.E. Asia) Pty Ltd, Singapore
Japan: United Publishers Services Ltd,
Tokyo

Printed in Singapore by
Toppan Printing Co. Pte Ltd
Designed by
ANU Graphic Design/Kirsty Morrison
Typeset by
TypoGraphics Communications Pty Ltd
Colour separations by
Toppan Printing Co. Pte Ltd

Contents

Kwork Kwork the Green Frog

Long ago in the Dreamtime, there lived a woman called Kwork Kwork. Kwork Kwork had three children who were called Pumarali, Tomataka and Pukataringa. Kwork Kwork loved the wet weather and whenever it rained she called her name to the sky, but if it was dry, she remained silent and waited for the rain to come.

Then there came a time when it did not rain for many years, and all the creeks and waterholes were dry. Kwork Kwork was very sad and finally she could not wait any longer for the rain to come, so she sent her three children into the sky. As they rose into the sky, they disappeared and dark storm clouds formed where they had been; Pumarali had changed into the lightning, Tomataka had changed into the thunder, and Pukataringa had become the rain. They made a great storm, filling the creeks and waterholes and flooding the land, so that Kwork Kwork was happy and called her name to her sons in the sky.

She changed into a Green Frog, and the Tiwi people today never hunt a green frog because they believe that if they do Kwork Kwork's children will flash and roar in the sky, and flood the land with rain.

Blue-Tongue Lizard and the Taipan

Blue-Tongue Lizard and his wife were camped near a swamp long ago. One day Blue-Tongue Lizard went to get some food, and while he was down at the swamp, he left his wife sitting under a shady tree. He had not been gone very long when Taipan passed by Blue-Tongue Lizard's camp. Taipan saw Blue-Tongue Lizard's wife sitting under the tree, and he decided he would steal her away from Blue-Tongue Lizard. He made her come with him and together they ran a long way away.

Taipan did not know that Black Bird had been watching him, and as soon as he ran away with Blue-Tongue Lizard's wife, Black Bird began singing out to Blue-Tongue Lizard, 'Your wife is gone, Taipan has taken her away', he cried. Blue-Tongue Lizard was still at the swamp getting food when he heard Black Bird's call. He went back to the shady tree where he had left his wife and saw she was gone. He put down his dilly bag which was full of food and made a fire. He cooked his food and after he had finished eating it, he went to get his spears. He found they had all been broken by Taipan. Then he found the tracks of his wife and Taipan and he followed them. Blue-Tongue Lizard followed their tracks until he came to a tree in which a freshly killed emu had been hung. It had been killed by Taipan and left there to be eaten that night. Blue-Tongue Lizard knew that Taipan and his wife must be nearby and he soon found them sitting near a river. When Taipan saw Blue-Tongue Lizard he ran to get his spears but Blue-Tongue Lizard had already broken them.

'We can fight with our teeth', said Blue-Tongue Lizard. Taipan agreed and the two of them fought wildly, each of them trying to get a hold of the other, until finally Blue-Tongue Lizard caught hold of Taipan's body in his powerful jaws, and bit him in half. With Taipan dead, Blue-Tongue Lizard took back his wife and together they returned to the swamp.

The Jabiru Man

Long ago, when Jabiru was a man, he went out hunting and speared a plains turkey. He brought it home to the camp and told two of his mothers-in-law to cook it. They cleaned the turkey and took out the giblets and the kidney fat as well. A little boy saw the kidney fat, which was a special food, and asked his mother to cook it for him, but his mother said to him, 'No, you are not allowed to eat the fat because it belongs to your cousin.' The little boy cried and cried to be given the kidney fat and eventually his mother cooked the fat and gave it to him.

The next morning the Jabiru man asked his little cousin, 'Did your mother give you some of the fat from the plains turkey?', and the little boy answered, 'Yes, it was very good.' Then the little boy's parents came to the Jabiru man and told him that they were going hunting and that they would leave their son with him.

When they had gone, the Jabiru man took the little boy with him to look for white fruit. They found a tree with a lot of the white fruit hanging from it, and many pieces which had fallen to the ground. The little boy started to pick up some of the fallen fruit but the Jabiru man said, 'Leave that bad fruit alone. We'll go in a bit further and find another tree.' So they went deeper into the bush and found another tall tree with white fruit hanging from it. The Jabiru man climbed the tree and when he got to the top, he told the little boy to stand in a clear place where he could see him. Then the Jabiru man picked some of the unripe fruit, which was as hard as rocks. To punish the little boy for eating his kidney fat, the Jabiru man started throwing the hard pieces of fruit at the little boy. Some of it hit him on the head, and the little boy cried and fell down on the ground.

Just then the little boy's mother and father came to the place and saw what had been happening. The father saw the Jabiru man in the tree and climbed up after him with his spear. He speared the Jabiru man through the neck and as he fell to the ground his wife hit him on the nose with her digging stick, flattening it. He changed into a large bird, the Jabiru, and the spear became his long neck and his beak. If you look at his beak today you will see where it was flattened by the digging stick long ago.

The Boy Who Became a White Cockatoo

Long ago there lived a man who had two sons. He was very old and he needed his sons to hunt for him, and every day he would sit under a tree while his two sons went far away to hunt. Late in the afternoon, the two sons would come back to their father and bring him food.

One day when the two sons were out hunting they came to a waterhole. They knew it was a sacred waterhole because their father had told them when they were young boys that they must keep away from it. One of the sons said: 'We must go back to our father with his food before he gets hungry' and so they left the sacred waterhole and went back to their father's camp. That night the two sons asked their father about the sacred waterhole but he only told them that they must not go there again.

The next day the two sons were out hunting again.

The younger son decided he would go back to the sacred waterhole and left his brother to hunt alone. When he reached the waterhole, he stood at its edge thinking about what his father had told him, and then he jumped into the water and swam to the other side. Once there, he got out of the water and sat at the edge of the waterhole, and as he did so, white feathers started growing all over his body. Soon he was covered with white feathers, his nose had changed into a beak and he became a white cockatoo.

He flew back to his father's camp and tried to speak to him, but his voice made only a strange loud crying sound. His father heard his cry and looked up, and as he saw the white cockatoo flying above him, he knew that it was his son and that he had disobeyed him by going back to the sacred waterhole.

The Emu and the Plains Turkey

Long ago, in the Dreamtime, Plains Turkey and Emu always went hunting together. But Emu was jealous of Plains Turkey because Plains Turkey had more children than she had. One morning, before they were due to go hunting, Emu hid all except two of her children in the bush, then, with just two of her children, she went over to Plains Turkey's camp. 'Where are all your other children?' asked Plains Turkey.

'I've killed them all except these two', lied Emu. But Plains Turkey believed her and she killed all of her children except two. When Plains Turkey had finished, Emu called to the children she had hidden, and when they came running out from behind the bushes, Plains Turkey was very angry and said to Emu, 'You told me a lie, sister.'

Emu didn't answer but took all of her children and went to dig for roots. Plains Turkey followed with her two children and also began digging for roots. Soon Plains Turkey's dilly bag was full of food, so she went back to her camp to cook the food. She made a fire and placed the roots in the hot coals, using a cooking stick to make a space for them and to cover the roots over with the coals. When she had finished her meal, she hid the cooking stick in the sand.

Not long after she had finished, Emu returned with her dilly bag full of roots and asked Plains Turkey for her cooking stick, but Plains Turkey said that she had used her wings because she hadn't been able to find the cooking stick. So Emu used her wings to push aside the coals and to cover them back over the roots, and as she did this the hot coals burnt her wings very badly. And ever since that time the Emu has had to walk along the ground and watch the Plains Turkey fly above her in the sky.

Yirrumarru, Ngarringa and Kilipurini

Ngarringa was the wife of Yirrumarru and the two of them lived in the land called Nguiu (Bathurst Island) during the Dreamtime. One day while Ngarringa was out gathering food, she met a man called Kilipurini. Kilipurini told Ngarringa that he was hungry so she gave him some food she had gathered. When Kilipurini had finished eating, he asked Ngarringa to stay with him, but she answered that her husband Yirrumarru would be very angry if she did. But Kilipurini made her stay.

When Ngarringa went back to her husband's camp she told him about Kilipurini, and Yirrumarru was angry, but he pretended that he did not know about it whenever he saw Kilipurini, and waited for a time when he could 'pay back' Kilipurini's insult.

The two men were out hunting one day when Yirrumarru saw some honey bees. They followed the bees to their tree and Yirrumarru asked Kilipurini to climb the tree and chop down the hollow branch where the bees had their nest. As Kilipurini climbed the tree, Yirrumarru kept telling him to climb higher and higher. When Kilipurini had reached the very top of the tree and could climb no higher, Yirrumarru shook the tree with all of his strength and Kilipurini crashed to the ground. The moment he hit the ground Kilipurini changed into a lizard and ran away. Yirrumarru changed into an eagle who still hunts the lizard, and his wife Ngarringa became a black cockatoo and never lived with him again.

It was in this way that the first Tiwi people in the Dreamtime became the animals of the land and the birds of the air, and why they remain our relatives today.

Purukupali

Purukupali was a strong leader of the Tiwi people, long ago. His wife's name was Waiyayi and they had a baby son whose name was Jinini. Purukupali had a brother called Japara who loved Purukupali's wife and often met secretly with her when she went out hunting food in the bush.

One day, after Purukupali had been out hunting all day, he asked his wife to bring him some water, so Waiyayi took a bowl made from dried mud and went to the creek to get some water for her husband. She took the baby Jinini with her.

As she was walking towards the creek she heard Japara, her lover, calling to her from the mangroves, so she left Jinini under the shade of a tree and went to Japara.

Soon the baby Jinini became thirsty and began crying for his mother, but Japara would not let Waiyayi go to him. Louder and louder the baby Jinini cried until Purukupali heard his son crying. Purukupali called out to his wife to see why Jinini was crying, but Japara held his hand over Waiyayi's mouth so that she could not answer him. Purukupali called again but still Japara would not let her answer, Purukupali then went looking for his wife and son and walked towards the creek. He found Jinini lying under the tree but he was dead, and then Purukupali knew that his wife was with his brother, Japara, and that the two of them were lovers. He carried his son back to his camp and while all of his people watched he laid his son's body under a tree. Then he went into the bush to make spears for his fight with Japara.

The lovers came back to the camp while Purukupali was still out in the bush, but when Waiyayi saw her dead son, she lay beside his body and cried. When Purukupali returned with the spears he had made, he beat Waiyayi for leaving Jinini to die while she went to her lover. While he was beating her, Japara came across to Purukupali and asked him if he could take Jinini's body up into the sky for three days and bring him back to life. But Purukupali replied, 'No! You won't take my son!' and picked up his spears. Japara ran off and came back with his own spears, ready to fight. The two brothers threw their spears at each other, but neither of them could hit the other as they were both very quick and could dodge the spears in flight. When their spears were finished, they fought with clubs until finally Purukupali struck his brother on the head and Japara fell to the ground.

What happened to Japara is another story, but Purukupali took the body of his son Jinini in his arms and carried him towards the sea. As he walked he called to his people to follow him. Then he stamped his foot on a rock and left his mark upon it and it still can be seen today. He stamped his feet again and made a great swirling lake and then, still carrying his son, he walked into the water and drowned. All the people of his tribe followed him and were drowned as well, except for Purukupali's wife, Waiyayi, who was left on the beach crying for her dead son, Jinini.

Japara and Wuruprenala

Wuruprenala was the sister of Purukupali and Japara and while her two brothers had fought over the death of Jinini, Wuruprenala had hidden behind some bushes and watched them fight. When Japara had been struck down by Purukupali, Wuruprenala had come out from behind the bushes and made a fire near Japara's body. It brought Japara back to life. Purukupali had laid down his clubs and, before he walked into the sea with his son's body, he first went over to his sister's fire. He took from the fire two burning sticks, a small one and a large one. He gave the large firestick to his sister, Wuruprenala, who changed into the Sun, and the small firestick he gave to Japara, who changed into the Moon.

Now Japara gives the light when it is dark and his sister, Wuruprenala, the Sun-Woman, is asleep. But when Wuruprenala wakes in the morning, she takes her firestick and moves through the sky and gives light to the land, until the end of the day. Then, at sunset, she paints herself red and makes the sky glow with colour until she falls asleep.

Pwanga the Spider Woman

Pwanga was a very clever woman who lived a long time ago. She made the first bark basket by chopping large pieces of bark from the trees and then heating them over the fire to make the pieces of bark flat. Then she would rub off the charcoal and make the bark smooth. Once this was done she made string from strips of bark fibre by rolling them together on her leg until they became one long piece of string. She had a needle made from a fish bone and she used the string to sew together two of the large flat pieces of bark. When she had finished the basket, her husband painted it and gave it to Purukapali for the pukaminni (burial) ceremonies.

Today, on our island, people still make baskets in this way, and Pwanga is a spider who lives in a home made from bark. She ties the strips of bark together with the string she makes from her body.

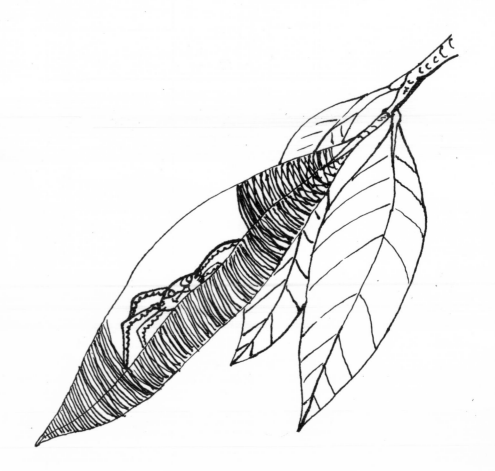

Water Rat and Squid

In the Dreamtime, when the animals were still people, a young man called Water Rat lived on a rocky island near Mornington Island. Water Rat didn't like the rocky island and wished that he could get across to Mornington Island and to the trees he could see in the distance. While he was sitting there feeling lonely and unhappy, another young man called Squid walked by. Squid noticed how unhappy Water Rat looked and asked him why he was unhappy, and Water Rat told him that he wanted to go across to Mornington Island but that it was too far for him to swim. Squid, who was a very good swimmer, then offered to take Water Rat across on his back, and although the sea was rough, they set off straight away.

As Squid swam with Water Rat on his back, the wind blew up and the waves grew bigger, sometimes splashing over Squid's head and washing his hair down over his face. Water Rat thought that this made Squid look very ugly and he laughed whenever it happened. But he did not tell Squid why he was laughing because he was frightened that Squid might throw him off and leave him in the sea. Squid heard Water Rat laughing and it made him feel uneasy, but he said nothing and continued swimming through the rough water towards Mornington Island. Finally, they reached the shore and they were both very cold, so they searched for wood to make a fire and warm themselves.

When they had the fire going and they had warmed themselves, Squid asked Water Rat why he had been laughing so much as they had been swimming across. Water Rat told Squid how the waves had washed hair all over his face and how ugly it had made him look, and it made Squid very angry to be made fun of by Water Rat while he had been helping him. Squid picked up a sharp stick and threw it at Water Rat which hit him at the bottom of his back. Water Rat took a black charred stick from the fire and threw it at Squid. It struck him on the back leaving a big black patch of charcoal.

Then they both changed into animals, and the stick in Water Rat's back became his long tail, while the charcoal on Squid's back became the ink he squirts out whenever he's annoyed or frightened.

Scrub Turkey and the Brown Pigeon

Long ago Scrub Turkey and Brown Pigeon were thirsty and were digging a well to find water. They had dug a deep hole but unknown to Scrub Turkey, Brown Pigeon had found a waterhole which he did not tell his friend about. Everytime it was Scrub Turkey's turn to dig at the bottom of the hole, Pigeon sneaked off to have a drink at his secret waterhole while Scrub Turkey got thirstier and thirstier.

After they had been digging a long time Scrub Turkey noticed that Pigeon did not seem to be as tired and thirsty as he should be and so the next time it was his turn to dig at the bottom of the hole, he did not go right to the bottom, but kept close to the top. He heard Pigeon walk away and so he got out of the hole and followed him. When Scrub Turkey saw Pigeon drinking at the waterhole he was angry at his friend's greediness. He said nothing but put a magic spell on Brown Pigeon and suddenly Brown Pigeon stopped drinking. Ever since that time the Brown Pigeon has never been able to drink in the daytime, and drinks only at night, even today.

Parumparuma

Parumparuma was a woman who lived in the Dreamtime. She lived happily with two men who were called Irrumarru and Mutati until one day Irrumarru took Parumparuma for a walk. This made Mutati wild and angry and he decided he would make a trap to punish Irrumarru. He went into the bush and found an old bandicoot's hole and in the hole he put some sharp pointed sticks and then covered them over with grass. Then he went back to his camp and waited for Parumparuma and Irrumarru to return.

Later that day, Irrumarru and Mutati were out hunting and Mutati led Irrumarru to the bandicoot's hole in which he had placed the sharp sticks. He told Irrumarru to jump in the hole before the bandicoots ran away, and when he did so the sharp sticks stuck into Irrumarru's feet. He cried out in pain and changed into a hawk, and flew away into the sky with the sharp sticks becoming his talons. Mutati then went back to Parumparuma and told her he wanted her to be his wife, but Parumparuma said 'No!' because she knew Mutati had killed Irrumarru. Once again, Mutati became very wild and angry and he hit Parumparuma over the head. The blows caused blood to run down the sides of her head and broke her neck, and as she died she changed into a plover bird, which is why the plover bird has a soft neck today and red patches on each side of its head.

The Story of Fire

Old Tasmanian legend, originally told to Joseph Milligan by an unknown story teller of the Oyster Bay tribe.

Long, long ago there was no fire in the land. No one had ever seen fire. People ate their food raw and had no fires to keep them warm at night. They were not able to straighten their spears or do the many other things they now do with fire.

It remained that way until one day two men were seen standing on top of a hill. The men were strangers to the people who watched them from below and as they watched, they saw the two men throw down fire. The fire came down like stars.

At first the people were frightened. They ran away, but after a while they returned. They took the fire and made a fire of wood. Never more was fire lost in the land.

The two men stayed in the land for a time. They camped near a sandy beach where they fished with their spears in the shallow water. As they walked along the water's edge one day, looking for fish, they were attacked by a giant sting-ray. Sting-ray had a very long spear, and on the spear were the bodies of two women. Sting-ray had killed the women while they were diving for crayfish. As it attacked the two men, they threw their spears and killed Sting-ray. They took the dead women from its long spear and made a fire of wood. On either side of the fire, they laid one of the dead women, and then they went into the bush and found some large blue ants. They placed the blue ants on each woman's chest and let the ants bite them angrily. The sharp bites and the heat of the fire revived the women so that they lived once more.

Soon after there came a fog, a thick, dark fog which turned the day into night. The two men and the two women passed through the fog and disappeared from the land to take their place in the sky.

On a clear night you can see the two men who brought fire to the land shining brightly in the northern sky, and beside them are two smaller stars, those of the two women who had been speared by the giant sting-ray in the time of the Dreaming.

The Bat and the Rainbow

Long ago, back in the Dreamtime, there lived a Bat. Bat was a very good dancer. All the animals loved to watch Bat dance. There also lived a Rainbow and Rainbow didn't like Bat. He had stolen two of Bat's wives. They were whistle ducks.

One day, some of the animals wanted to have a corroboree so they had a meeting to talk about it. They invited all the other animals of the bush and Bat came too. Rainbow was there as well and when Bat saw Rainbow lying down and the two whistle ducks fanning him, he be came very angry. He said to himself, 'I will kill Rainbow and bring back my wives'.

After the meeting, all the animals went back to their homes. Bat also went back to his home determined to kill Rainbow. The next morning he went to a high hill to find a stone to make a spearhead. He needed a very sharp stone and he tested many stones. He did this by cutting his nose to see how sharp each stone was. He tried and tried until at last he found one which he again tried on his nose. This time the stone cut his nose right off, which is why Bat has no nose today, but Bat was happy because he had a stone sharp enough to make a spearhead.

The day of the big corroboree arrived and all the animals came. Rainbow and the whistle ducks came too. Bat began to dance. He danced and danced until it was almost morning and all the animals had gone to sleep. Then Bat pretended to go to sleep too until he was sure that Rainbow and the whistle ducks were sound asleep.

When all was quiet and everyone was asleep, Bat crept up and got his spear from where he had hidden it and then stealthily went back to Rainbow and speared him. Rainbow roared with pain and the blood ran down his side. The animals awoke and saw him rolling over and over, and they flew away everywhere. Bat took back the two whistle ducks for his wives as Rainbow rolled into a waterhole and sank. Rainbow lives there today and sometimes when it rains he rises from the waterhole and arches his blood-stained body through the sky.

The River which was made from Tears

Once there lived a great hunter who found a giant brolga with a broken wing. At first the hunter felt frightened and tried to run away, but then he felt sorry for the brolga so he went up to the brolga and asked kindly how the wing was broken. The brolga told the hunter his story and as he did so great tears fell from the brolga's large sad eyes. The tears fell into the tracks he had made while he had crawled along in pain, and each tear was as big as the water of a billabong. They turned into cool fresh water and formed a river, flowing very fast along the brolga's tracks.

After he had told his story, the poor brolga died of sorrow and woe and the hunter rose into the sky and became the Morning Star, where he watches over the poor brolga.

The river which was made from the brolga's tears is called the Giddys River today and is not far from Yirrkala in the Northern Territory.